Treasures by the Sea

By Cathy Fosnot

New Perspectives on Learning, LLC
1194 Ocean Avenue
New London, CT 06320

The photographs appearing on pages 3 and 4 are from a series entitled *Josie Dancing with the Wave* produced by Julie Branby and are published with permission of the photographer.

ISBN-13: 978-1-7320437-6-3

Treasures by the Sea

It was finally summer. Josie, Maia, Cole, and Harrison loved summer because they knew they would soon get to visit their grandma at her home by the sea. They would get to jump and splash in the waves, build sand castles, dig deep holes, and walk along the shore with the seagulls.

But most of all, the children loved the long early morning walks with Grandma. They would all take pails and walk slowly along the shore looking for treasures for their collections. "Collections of treasures can be very special, but you have to look closely within," Grandma would say with a twinkle in her eye. "At first look, it seems like you have just a bunch of shells, glass, or rocks. But if you look again—very, very closely within—you can see the most beautiful, wondrous things. Each piece is a unique gem, different from the others, and sometimes you find something so special it is a real treasure to keep close and marvel at."

One day, Cole even saw a crab when he looked closely within. Do you see it?

Cole isn't keen on collecting crabs, though. He likes to collect shells and arrange them in interesting ways.

Grandma thinks these two shells are real treasures. "They look like they are talking to each other," she says. "Just imagine the stories they might be telling."

Sometimes Cole sorts his shells by color. He has yellow, white, dark blue, brown, and even some orange shells. But sorting by color is difficult because one of his orange shells is so light it is almost white. And one orange shell has yellow on it, too. Should it go with the yellow shells, or the orange shells?

Sometimes Cole sorts in other ways. Once he put 5 of his treasures together because they all were sort of the same shape—like ovals. He also thought maybe sea creatures had lived in them. But then he thought probably sea creatures had lived in all his shells; that would be a very big set and not a useful category. So he had another idea. He made this set of shells into two sets.

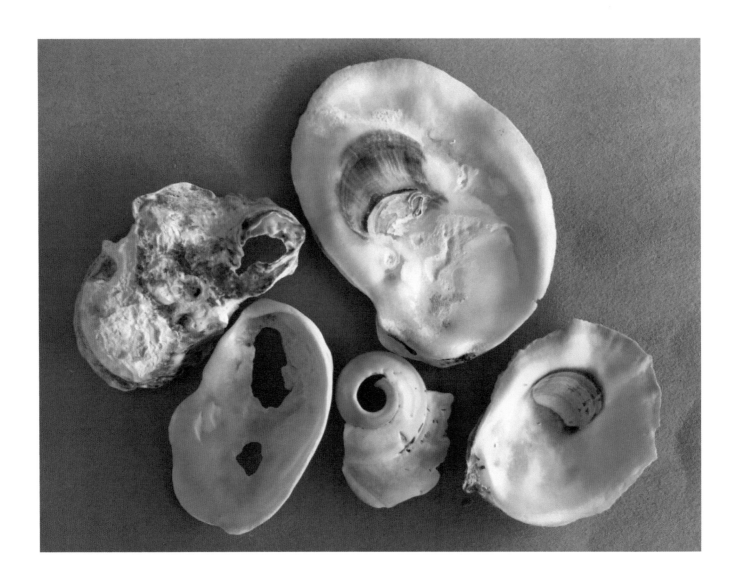

Now one set has 3 shells and the other has 2. Can you tell what categories Cole is thinking of now?

One day Cole made this set. He called his set "shells with dots" and arranged them on a pretty sheet of paper with dots! Then he put all the other shells in a big set and labeled it "shells with no dots."

Shells With Dots

Shells With No Dots

Harrison is not so keen on collecting shells. He likes to collect beach stones. He likes to throw them, skimming them across the water and counting the times he can make each stone jump.

Harrison likes to sort his stones into two piles: flat stones and non-flat stones. He especially likes the flat stones because he can make them jump many times across the water.

The non-flat stones usually just sink with a big splash!

Some of Harrison's non-flat stones are jagged and pointy, and some are smoother and round from being tossed about in the waves. Some have specks of white quartz and black mica that glisten in the sun like diamonds, and some don't.

One day, Harrison made a set called "stones with lines."

Maia and Josie like to collect sea glass. So far, they have found teal, white, blue, brown, and green sea glass. "Which color has more pieces?" Josie wondered, "and why haven't we found any red beach glass yet?"

To investigate, they sorted their collection of sea glass by color and made separate piles so they could count each and compare the sets.

Maia likes the teal sea glass the most. When she looked within her collection, like Grandma had suggested, each one was so special. Some had been beaten by crashing waves until they were round and felt almost sandy. Others were smooth, hard, and still sharp. They glistened in the sun like magic. Some were pieces of bottlenecks and others were not. Some even had letters. Maia wondered what the letters said and what the bottles had been used for before landing in the ocean and breaking into pieces.

One day, Maia decided to sort her collection of sea glass into two groups: bottlenecks and non-bottlenecks. Then she labeled her sets.

bottlenecks

non-bottlenecks

Josie became fascinated with the letters. Then she noticed that some of the sea glass had numerals on them, not letters! Can you tell which is which?

"Hmmm…" Josie wondered. "Will I find more pieces of sea glass with letters, or more pieces of sea glass with numerals?" To investigate, Josie sorted through her whole collection of sea glass. She found 6 pieces of sea glass with letters and 5 pieces of sea glass with numerals.

Josie decided to make a display of her findings. She arranged her sets in two straight lines, right next to each other. On the left she put her 6 pieces of sea glass with letters, and on the right she put her 5 pieces of sea glass with numerals.

But something was now strange. The lines looked like they were the same length! "But they can't be the same. One has 6 and the other only has 5. I'm sure 6 is one more than 5. Why do they look like the same amount?" Josie wondered.

What had gone wrong? Why do the lines look like they have the same number?

| **Sea Glass with Letters** | **Sea Glass with Numerals** |

Grandma likes to collect treasures, but she loves walking on the beach with her grandchildren most of all. "People are treasures, too," she says, "and every moment with you is a treasure I will keep in my mind forever!"

About the Author:

Cathy Fosnot is Professor Emerita of Childhood Education at the City College of New York where she founded the NSF-funded center, Mathematics in the City. She is the lead author of the Contexts for Learning Mathematics series and the Young Mathematicians at Work series. In 2004 she received the Teacher of the Year Award from CCNY. She retired from the college in 2010 and currently serves as the Senior Content Consultant for the award-winning internet math environment, DreamBox Learning, and is President of New Perspectives on Learning, New Perspectives on Assessment, and New Perspectives Online. In September of 2016 she released a new book, Conferring with Young Mathematicians at Work: Making Moments Matter.

Printed in Great Britain
by Amazon